W

HEN Captain Arthur Phillip R.N. selected Sydney Cove as a site for the penal colony to be established in New South Wales nothing could have been further from his thoughts than that he was within a stone's throw of a site on which, one day, would stand the stately arches and glistening contours of a noble pile — an epic monument to the performing arts.

It was late afternoon of January 25, 1788· hot mid-summer. The wooded hills surrounding the little bay seemed strangely dark, a sombre contrast with the vivid green trees and meadows of Britain. As the sun went down the darkness deepened and the company on the "Supply" knew they were at their long journey's end, in the great unknown Land of the South.

On January 26 the Union Jack was unfurled at the site of the landing, the King's health was drunk, and a toast was offered to the success of the new Colony.

FOLLOWING the arrival from Botany Bay of the other vessels of the First Fleet, Phillip began the task of unloading the ships — officers and men assembled the convict prisoners, and the livestock, stores and tools to establish the settlement were taken ashore.

The stock was landed on the eastern side of the Cove, where, at the northern extremity, a rocky outcrop was separated from the mainland by a narrow channel.

In 1789, Governor Phillip, hoping to learn more of the aborigines' customs and language, had an aboriginal, Bennelong, brought to the settlement. To continue to establish friendly intercourse with the natives Governor Phillip had built a house 12 feet square on the eastern extremity of Sydney Cove — which became known as Bennelong Point.

When Phillip returned to England in 1792, he took Bennelong with him, so apt a pupil had he become in learning the ways of civilisation. In London, flamboyantly adopting the dress and mannerisms of an 18th century dandy, Bennelong was doubtless intrigued by the elegant music of the period, so far from the primitive chants of his aboriginal tribesmen.

BY New Year's Day, 1789, the Colony's first forti-
fication, a small redoubt on Bennelong Point,
held eight pieces of ordnance from the "Sirius."
In 1791, the redoubt demolished, a storehouse
was erected on the site. The building, 80 feet by
24 feet, with a loft, was the largest then constructed. Later in 1798, the storehouse was replaced by a crescent battery where, previously,
native corroborees had been seen by members of
the First Fleet who had shown their appreciation
of the singing and dancing, and the tapping
together of wooden sticks, by cries of "boojery
carib-berie" — a good dance ....

N 1810 Lt-Colonel Lachlan Macquarie took up his appointment as Governor of the Colony and in the decade that followed, laid the foundations of the future City of Sydney, later to become the capital of the State of New South Wales. Many notable thoroughfares and buildings were named after him; among them, Fort Macquarie.

Completed in January, 1821, the Fort, designed by Francis Greenway, was constructed of stone hewn from an outcrop which the locals called the Tarpeian Rock, a classical allusion to the precipitous Capitoline Hill in Rome from which, in the time of the Caesars, criminals were hurled to their deaths.

The site, naturally enough, was Bennelong Point. For eighty years the Fort stood, a silent tribute to the convicts who slaved to build it in the early days of the Colony, its guns never fired in anger, the people it guarded never in need of defence.

AT the turn of the century Fort Macquarie was demolished and replaced by a Tram Depot. However, the romance of the nineteenth century fortress was preserved, to some degree, in the name and design of the new rectangular building with its crenellated towers and convex bay-walls.

Constructed of red brick and sandstone the new building faced the Harbour, a grassy tree-lined reserve separating it from the sea wall.

The Fort Macquarie Depot, opened on August 10, 1902, became the terminus etc. of the Belmore-Circular Quay electric tram line which came down Castlereagh and Bligh Streets and circled the building on its way from and to the suburbs.

Later, George Street routes were added and passengers on trams approached Bennelong Point past the busy wharves of the Circular Quay Ferry terminal. The blue coated conductors who punched their tickets for the first half of the century could never know that the Fort was fated, in years to come, to be razed to the ground — that in the great building that was to replace it, conductors of a very different kind would dominate the scene.

THE death knell of the Tram Depot was sounded when Eugene Goossens, Resident Conductor of the Sydney Symphony Orchestra and Director of the New South Wales Conservatorium of Music, had a sudden inspiration.

The need for an Opera House had been on his mind for several years and he had often pondered over the most desirable site for such a building.

Strolling along the lawned foreshore of Farm Cove, he was looking over Fort Macquarie Depot towards the Harbour Bridge, and the thought struck him, what a breathtaking spectacle it would be — a great gleaming structure occupying the whole of Bennelong Point. In its vast interior would be staged splendid operas; there the world's greatest orchestras would play! Approaching Circular Quay from the Heads, he mused, "First you will see the Opera House, then you will see the Bridge!".

In 1955 Goossens was appointed to a committee of five to advise the Government if the building of an Opera House was practicable, and where it might be placed.

Here was his opportunity. Convinced that this was one of the world's most magnificent sites, he and his colleagues reported to the Government, "There is no other place to equal this. The Opera House must be built on Bennelong Point!"

The Story of
"SYDNEY BUILDS AN OPERA HOUSE"
begins with the arrival of the
First Fleet at Sydney Cove
in January 1788, and ends with the
completion of the Sydney Opera House
in September 1973.

A companion Book
"SYDNEY HAS AN OPERA HOUSE"
will be published in December 1973.
It will present a story
of the performing arts in Sydney,
from the first performance
by a group of convicts in 1789,
to the spectacular Celebrations
to mark the Official Opening
of the Sydney Opera House
by Her Majesty Queen Elizabeth II
on October 20, 1973.

Edited By
Oswald L. Ziegler
Photography by
Max Dupain
Illustrations by
Arthur Boothroyd
Layout and Designed by
Alan D. Ziegler
Printed by
Times Printers Sdn. Bhd. Singapore
Published by
© **Oswald Ziegler Publications Pty. Ltd. 1973**
ISBN 0 909586 05 5

PRODUCED AND PUBLISHED BY

SYDNEY BUILDS AN OPERA HOUSE

OSWALD ZIEGLER PUBLICATIONS PTY. LTD. SYDNEY, AUSTRALIA.

The Hon. Sir Robert William Askin, K.C.M.G., M.L.A.,
Premier and Treasurer of New South Wales.

Foreword

THE opening of the Sydney Opera House by Her Majesty Queen Elizabeth II on October 20, 1973, will be one of the most memorable occasions in the history of Australia.

It will be the culmination of almost twenty years of hoping, planning and striving towards the completion of a cultural complex unique in the annals of the performing arts.

Almost twenty years ago the Government of the day passed a Bill to construct an Opera House. The site was to be Bennelong Point, a site unexcelled for sheer beauty in any other city of the world.

The most eminent architects of all nations were invited to submit their ideas, and from them was chosen a design, the like of which had never been seen before. Jørn Utzon, a relatively little known Dane, devised it, and I express my admiration for his conception.

Builders and contractors were appointed and the great project was begun.

As the work progressed, the magnitude of the undertaking and the unusual structural features it involved created a never-ending stream of problems, and many months were spent in trying to solve them.

When my Government was elected to office in 1965 we were faced with situations that threatened to jeopardize the entire operation. The resignation of Jørn Utzon meant that a successor needed to be found, and we adopted the recommendation of the Royal Institute of Architects that a group of three of Sydney's leading architects be commissioned to reorganise the production programme and complete the building.

To these men and the many others whom they co-opted to make a success of their prodigious task, the builders, the engineers, the tradesmen whose skills are manifest in the building, and the members of the Sydney Opera House Trust who devoted so much of their time advising and helping in the planning, I pay the highest tribute.

This book tells the story of the Sydney Opera House in accurate and appealing style.

SYDNEY
August, 1973

R.W. ASKIN
Premier.

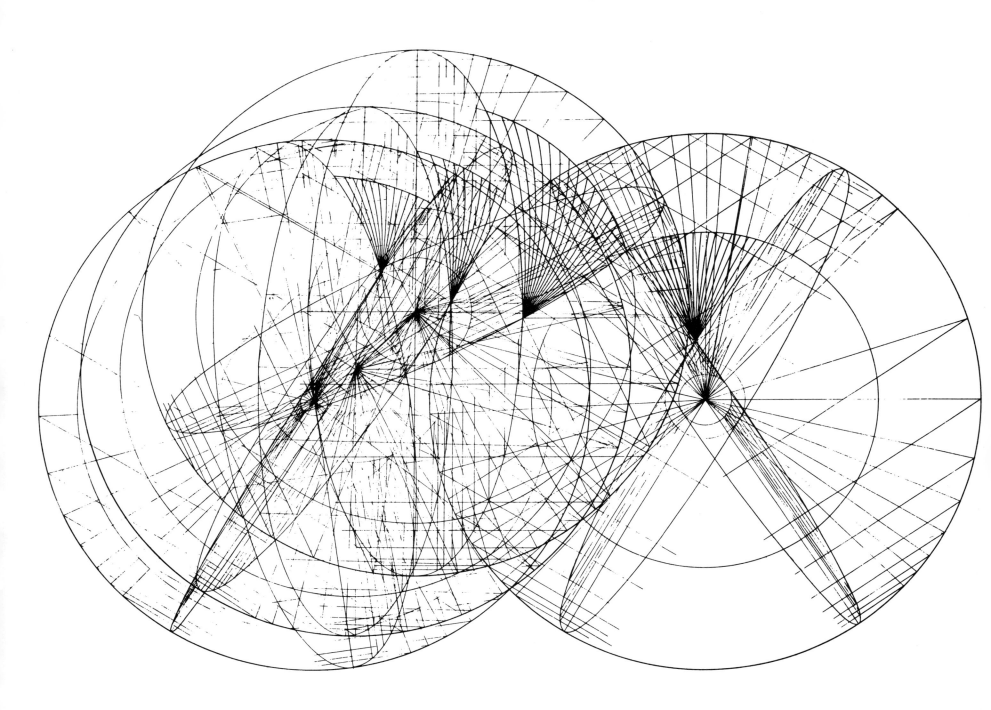

Contents

20 The Conception

24 World Competition

26 Utzon

32 On the Drawing Board

34 Problems

36 Construction

64 The Masterpiece

82 Financed by Lottery

83 The Sydney Opera House Trust

84 A Tribute

The Hon. J. J. Cahill, M.L.A.,
Premier and Treasurer of New South Wales
1952 - 1959.

The Conception

N November 30, 1954, the Premier of New South Wales, the Hon. J.J. Cahill, M.L.A., announced the appointment of a Committee to advise the Government on the building of "an Opera House".

With this step Australia was to acquire a priceless heritage and for the people of New South Wales a new era began in the cultural life of the State.

One of the greatest achievements of this age, the construction of the Sydney Opera House demanded infinite patience and unceasing co-operation between architects, engineers, building technicians and contractors for almost two decades.

Below:
Left to right:
Sir Charles Moses, Kt. C.B.E.
Sir Eugene Goossens, Kt.,
Prof. Henry Ingham Ashworth, O.B.E.

Opposite page:
Mr. Stanley Haviland, C.B.E.
Mr. Roy Hendy, C.M.G.

THE Premier's Committee comprised Mr. Stanley Haviland, C.B.E. as Chairman, then Under-Secretary for Local Government and later President of the Sydney Water Board; Professor Henry Ingham Ashworth, O.B.E., M.A., B.Arch., F.R.I.B.A., P.P., F.R.A.I.A., Hon. F.R.A.I.C., M.A.P.I., then Professor of Architecture at the University of Sydney and later Dean of the Faculty; Mr. Charles Moses, (now Sir Charles Moses, Kt., C.B.E.) then General Manager of the Australian Broadcasting Commission and now Secretary-General of the Asian Broadcasting Union; Mr. (later Sir) Eugene Goossens, Resident Conductor of the Sydney Symphony Orchestra and Director of the N.S.W. State Conservatorium of Music; and Mr. Roy Hendy, C.M.G., then Town Clerk of Sydney.

This group of men was asked to choose a suitable site and provide a design that would satisfy functional needs and appeal to the tastes of the public. The original Committee was later expanded and became the Opera House Executive Committee.

Appointed by the Royal Australian Institute of Architects, Professor Ashworth, (Professor of Architecture and Dean at University of Sydney and later University of New South Wales), Professor Denis Winston, (Professor of Town and Country Planning at Sydney University and later Dean of the Faculty of Architecture) and Mr. Walter Bunning, (a leading Sydney Architect and Chairman of the State Planning Advisory Committee), investigated some thirty sites; but Bennelong Point was finally chosen for its historic background and, above all, for its magnificent aspect overlooking one of the finest harbours in the world.

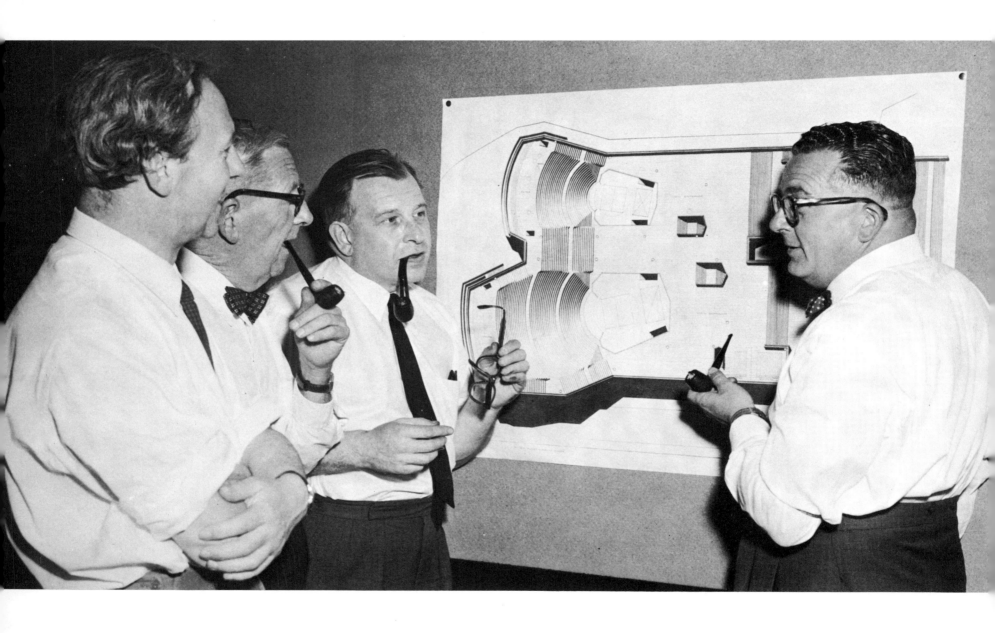

The four Assessors
discussing the design
of the winning submission of the
International Competition.

From left to right:
Mr. Eero Saarinen, Dr. Cobden Parkes,
and Sir Leslie Martin with
Prof. H. Ingham Ashworth.

World Competition

ON September 13, 1955, Mr. Cahill announced that an international competition would be held, open to architects of every country; from the submissions received, the New South Wales Government would select a design worthy of the Commonwealth's finest Opera House.

Details of the competition were set out in a twenty-five page booklet which, although the words "proposed national opera house" were used, made it clear that opera was not to be the only, or even the primary purpose of the building.

The conditions stipulated that provision must be made for a large hall to seat between 3,000 and 3,500 people and a small hall to seat about 1,200.

The large hall would be designed for the following purposes:

(a)   Symphony concerts (including organ music and solo recitals).
(b)   Large scale opera.
(c)   Ballet and dance performances.
(d)   Choral concerts.
(e)   Pageants and mass meetings.

The small hall would be designed for:

(a)   Dramatic presentations.
(b)   Intimate opera.
(c)   Chamber music.
(d)   Concerts and recitals.
(e)   Lectures.

The conditions specifically stated:

> "The requirements ... have been listed in order of priority with respect to the attention which should be given to their specialised building needs ...

> "Compromises which will prejudice the entirely satisfactory performance of a function with a higher priority in the above list should not be made".

The competition attracted enquiries from all over the world. Two hundred and thirty-three designs were submitted from thirty-two countries, notably the U.S.A., Great Britain, West Germany, France, Denmark, Japan and Australia.

The judges of the competition were Eero Saarinen, the celebrated American architect; Dr. J.L. (later Sir Leslie) Martin, Professor of Architecture at the University of Cambridge; Professor H. Ingham Ashworth and the N.S.W. Government architect, Dr. Cobden Parkes. They conducted their deliberations in the Sydney Art Gallery.

The Premier announced the decision of the judges to a select audience at the Art Gallery on January 29, 1957. The first prize was awarded for a design submitted by 38-years-old Danish architect Jørn Utzon. Second prize was won by an American group and an English firm gained third award.

Utzon

SKETCH OF JORN UTZON'S WINNING DESIGN

ALTHOUGH Jørn Utzon had won architectural competitions in Denmark, he was unknown to most Australian architects. He lived with his family near Hellebaek, a small village on Denmark's northern sea coast, a few miles from the famous old ship-building town of Helsingfor; its anglicised name is Elsinore.

Here still stands the castle which Shakespeare used as the setting for his famous play, "Hamlet". Like "the melancholy Dane", Utzon used to wander over the ramparts of the castle when he was a boy and in planning the Sydney Opera House, he was able to envisage how it, too, would appear

built on the water's edge. Utzon had travelled widely and was greatly interested in the plinth formation of the ancient Mayan temples of Mexico. The effect of this influence is obvious in the strong horizontal lines he introduced in his Sydney Opera House podium.

As an imaginative architect Utzon had a touch of genius, and only a genius could have designed so unique a building as he planned for Bennelong Point. But as an executant architect his experience was limited; he had never been required to design and supervise the construction of any big building from start to finish. Writing of Utzon, the noted architectural teacher and historian Siegfried Gledion stated "almost the only things Utzon had build were 63 ... houses near Elsinore and a smaller housing project near Fredensborg".

Utzon won the competition with a set of sketches, preliminary plans and elevations. In their summary, the judges wrote this comment: "The drawings submitted are simple to the point of being diagramatic. Nevertheless, as we have returned again and again to the study of these drawings, we are convinced that they present a concept of an opera house which is capable of being one of the great buildings of the world".

Above:

The formal perspective drawing produced by Mr. Arthur Baldwinson, architect, interpreting Jørn Utzon's competition plans.

Opposite Page:

A sketch of the proposed Opera House prepared by celebrated architect, Eero Saarinen, an Assessor of the designs submitted for the International Competition. The object of the sketch was to assist the Assessors in their deliberations.

a

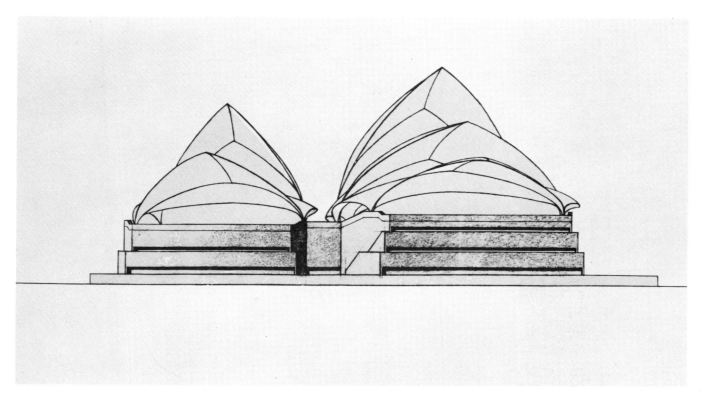

b

C

Photographs of
Jørn Utzon's original competition
drawings:-
(a) East elevation
     showing the massive podium
     and the light,
     exciting roof forms
(b) north elevation
(c) perspective view
     looking up the steps of the
     main podium between the Major Hall
     and the Minor Hall.

Above:
A general perspective
of the circular design submitted
by an American group,
awarded second prize in the
International Competition.

Right:
Two sections through the Main Building

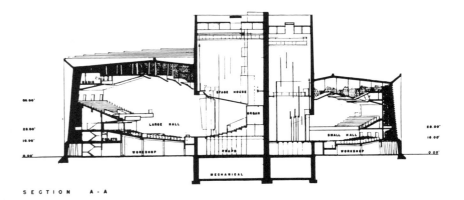

SECTION A-A

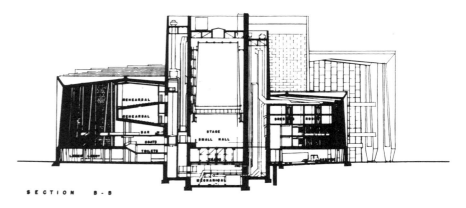

SECTION B-B

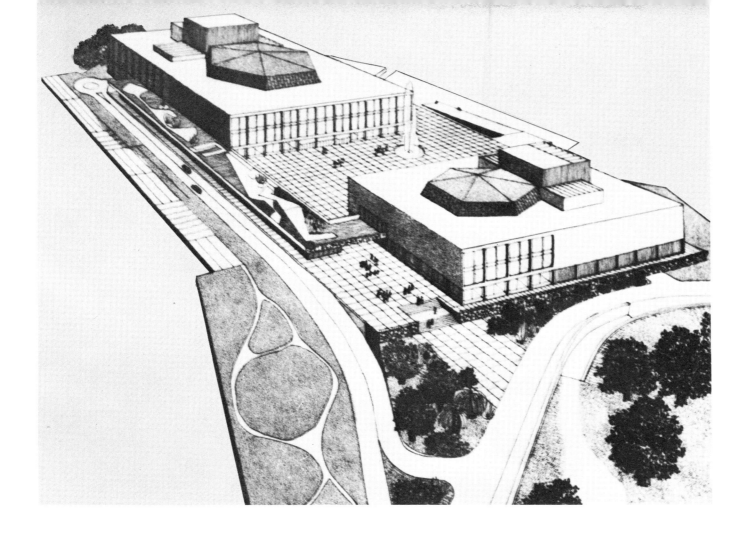

The perspective drawing
of a rectangular design submitted
by an English firm,
and awarded third prize in the
International Competition.

On the Drawing Board

ARCHITECTS, engineers and stage producers who saw those prize winning sketches realised that the sheer sculptural beauty of the building placed it in a category of its own. Restricted by the waters of the Harbour, Utzon planned to use the maximum width and depth available for the stages of his two great halls, by moving scenery on and off the vertical lifts leading down to huge storage spaces below. The roof vaults were big and boldly curved and in the light of previous experience in shell concrete work it seemed that their construction would be feasible. However, as the work progressed so many problems arose that it was doubtful if they could be solved by any known structural technology. The Cahill Government might well have chosen one of the simpler — but less splendid — second or third prize winning designs, but if Utzon had shown extraordinary imagination in conceiving his Opera House, so also did the Government in commissioning it.

A photograph of
Jørn Utzon's original model
brought from Denmark.
The model shows
the Major Hall and the Minor Hall,
and the location
of the Restaurant on the
stepped platform.

Opposite page
Jørn Utzon with
Professor N. J. Andersson
at the site of the
Sydney Opera House.

The Architects for Stage 111,
Hall, Todd and Littlemore.
From left to right:
Peter B. Hall, David S.
Littlemore, Lionel M. Todd.

Throughout the course of its construction, the Opera House was a continual source of interest to architects and engineers the world over. All who participated in the project found that their knowledge and skill were tested to the full: there were few precedents to serve as guides to its many unusual constructional features. The engineers, Ove Arup and Partners, the British based international structural consultants appointed at the suggestion of Jørn Utzon, faced immense tasks.

The Minister for Public Works in the Cahill Government, Mr. P.N. Ryan, first proposed that the Opera House be built in two stages, but as time went on it was considered more practicable to undertake the work in three stages:

Stage I.   Foundations and base.
Stage II.   Roof shells.
Stage III.   Finishing, equipment and furnishing.

Preliminary work began in May 1958, with the sinking of test bores by the N.S.W. Maritime Services Board, and on February 4, 1959, the State Cabinet accepted the tender of Civil and Civic Contractors Pty.Ltd., of Sydney for the first stage of construction. Earth moving began on March 2, 1959.

Mr. Cahill took an active interest in the progress of Stage I, and it was a matter of great regret that he did not live to see the commencement of Stages II and III. The Premier died in office in October 1959.

The State elections of May 1965 brought in a new Government, led by Mr. R.W. Askin, M.L.A., (later to become Sir Robert) and the Hon. Davis Hughes, M.L.A was given the portfolio of Minister for Public Works and was thus the new Constructing Authority.

Problems

AT the close of February 1966, Jørn Utzon announced his decision to retire from the project.

Since the time when the Hon. J.J. Cahill informed Parliament, in 1956, that the Opera House would be built at an estimated cost of £4,500,000 (A$9,000,000), that figure had risen by 1965 to more than £25,000,000 and the Government was becoming concerned at possible repercussions.

When asked to commit himself to a likely completion date and probable final cost Jørn Utzon was not prepared to do so.

Much of the work was still in experimental stages and although Mr. Hughes declared that the time had passed for experimenting and that conventional methods of construction must be adopted, Mr. Utzon was emphatic that it was impossible to use conventional methods for so unique a project. His refusal to forecast dates and costs led to an impasse.

The Government believed that in its responsibility to the people, it had no alternative but to accept Mr. Utzon's resignation. Despite the fierce controversy that arose at the time, particularly between cultural sections of the community, it is now generally conceded that the Government took the only logical course and the splendid building that now stands on Bennelong Point completely vindicates the decision of Premier Sir Robert Askin and his Ministers.

In April 1966, after the resignation of Jørn Utzon the Government appointed a new team of architects to complete the project. The appointees were: Peter B. Hall, architect; Lionel Todd, representing the firm of Hanson, Todd and Partners, architects; David Littlemore, of Rudder, Littlemore and Rudder,

Opposite page:

From a sphere ...
came the shells

Below:

A model of the Major Hall as originally planned by Jørn Utzon for the presentation of Opera and Music.

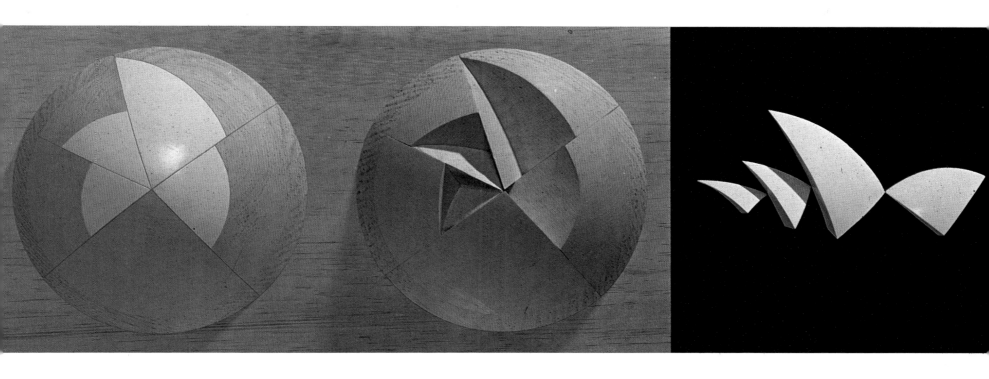

architects; and Edward H. Farmer, the Government architect, as adviser to the Minister for Public Works.

Their first task was to prepare a comprehensive review of the project: the work already completed and the work still to be done. The Government re-established its agreements with the structural engineers, Ove Arup and Partners, and engaged other consultants and specialists: electrical engineers, Julius Poole and Gibson of Sydney; Steensen Varning, Mechanical Engineers of Denmark; Professor Unruh of Germany, specialist in stage techniques; and Dr. Wilhelm L.Jordan, an international authority on acoustics. Later in the year 1966 Ben Schlanger, a noted theatre consultant of New York was also added to the team to help in re-programming the project.

The Jørn Utzon plan for the interior of the complex and its multiple functions was drastically revised: what would it contain; how many halls and their multi-purpose uses; what facilities and services for the public — particularly air conditioning; what services and facilities would be needed for staff and performers. Following a careful analysis, a new production programme was formulated, submitted to and approved by the Government.

The most fundamental change recommended was that the original design combining Concert Hall and Opera Theatre be abandoned.

Such a combination was technically difficult; it involved inevitable acoustic compromises and presented serious problems in seating and management.

Among the many other items listed were changes in the seating capacities of the various halls. Utzon's original accommodation for 1,800 in the Concert Hall was increased to 2,700; the Opera Theatre from 1,200 to 1,550; the Drama Theatre remained at 550; the Music Room increased from 200 to 420, and the Reception Hall to 200. Also replanned were the Rehearsing Hall and the Restaurants, and another Rehearsal Room and an Exhibition Hall of 7,000 square feet were provided.

In 1968, the architects and consultants presented a budget for the expenditure of $85,000,000, with a target for completion by the end of 1972.

LIKE some strange sailing craft about to take off on a mythical voyage, the Opera House is surmounted by three articulated roof systems billowing from its massive base. From some angles they look like gigantic shells.

The base of the complex, the podium, is surface-covered with a veneer of pink-grey reconstituted granite quarried at Tarana in the Blue Mountains of New South Wales. It measures 600 feet in length and 312 feet wide at its southern end projected towards Government House. Over all, it covers 4½ acres. The entire structure rests on a Tarpeian rock bed of sandstone found at water level, in which are set 550 concrete piers, each 3 feet in diameter. The highest point of the podium is 66 feet above mean sea-level.

From the podium rise a double row of high curving spined dome-like structures. These are the roofs of the stages, auditoria and foyers of the Concert Hall and the nearly parallel adjacent Opera Theatre. Their construction, which constituted Stage II of the

Construction

The Tram Depot
Bennelong Point in 1958,
before the commencement of
the building of the
Sydney Opera House.
1959. The site is cleared and
construction begins.

The completion of
Stage 1 of construction.
The podium as it appeared
from the air above Sydney Cove
and from the foot of
Ceremonial Steps.

mighty project, fully tested the technical and manual skills of the principal contractors, M.R. Hornibrook (NSW) Pty.Ltd., particularly the delicate placing of each section to achieve the highest degree of accuracy.

Soon after Stage II began, Ove Arup appointed a partner, Mr. M.R. Lewis, to take charge of operations on the site.

It took six years, more than 2,000 computer-hours and 350,000 man-hours, to perfect the designing of these intricate roof systems. Together they comprise 2,194 precast segments that, in their joining, present a vision of synchronised beauty.

The roof system housing the Concert Hall and its foyers — the western or Harbour Bridge side of the complex — is made up of four concrete vaults each formed by articulated

Sculptural post-tensioned beams
providing troughs for above-surface
water run-off and to support podium
slabs forming pavement.

Artistry in structural
design is in evidence everywhere.
A workman is silhouetted
against the concrete beams
which form the ceiling of the
main access stairs from the
vehicular concourse to the
Box Office foyer.
Even in the early stages
of construction, the shells show
signs of stately beauty.

The sails take shape
as precast beam segments are
placed in position in Stage 11
of construction. On-site
precasting of concrete
segments is carried out
in the foreground
while assembly is in progress
on the podium.

"shells". Together they have maximum measurements of 400 feet from north to south and 176 feet from east to west. The top of the tallest shell soars 221 feet above mean sea-level — the height of a 22-storey office building. Beneath four shells on the eastern side of the complex is the Opera Theatre. Over all, they cover an area of 352 feet by 128 feet, the tallest shell reaching to a height of 186 feet above mean sea-level.

Within the roof vaults of the shells are opposing rows of concrete ribs, each precision-cast to fit the upward curve of its neighbour. Architectural and engineering skills made it possible to pre-fabricate these huge sections from parts made by mass production techniques. The forms were constructed of plywood and covered with polyester to give a high finish. They were then coated with

Precast rib segments
moved to a point of access,
are raised into position to form
the fan-like shape of the roofs;
a unique feature of the
Sydney Opera House.
On completion
of each rib section
the segments are locked together
with high-tensile
steel cables, joining the whole
as one unit.

In the process of
precasting the concrete rib
sections, the reinforcement is
lowered into a mould
and positioned preparatory
to pouring the concrete.

Following
the period of ''curing'',
the framework is
removed and the concrete
rib segment is raised
for placement.

A never ending source of interest
to Sydney-siders, the Opera House
now well into Stage II of construction
is viewed from the
Overseas Passenger Terminal
on the western shores
of Sydney Cove.

Work in progress
completing the A1, A2, B1
and B2 shell roofs
as seen from Man-O'-War Steps.
The concrete sail
structure of the shell roofs
is ready to receive the
surface tiles.

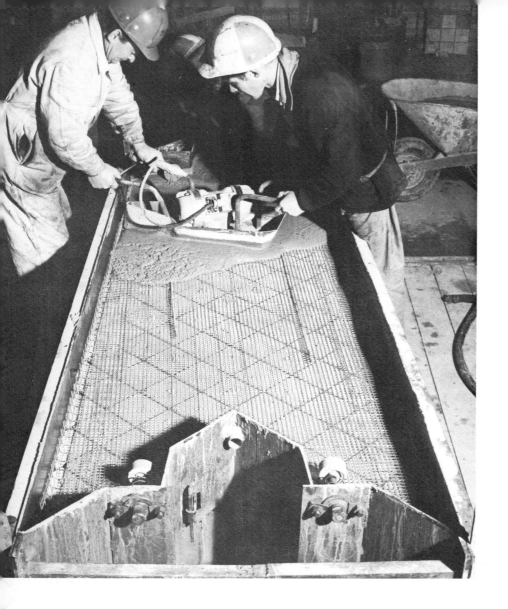

Shellmoid compound — made by the Shell Company of Australia — to allow them to be stripped cleanly from the cast concrete. The segments of each rib were 15 feet long. Five such segments were cast in a single mould, only the crown tips being of separate moulding. The last segment of the last rib was placed in position in mid-January, 1967 — three years and two months after the commencement of the Second Stage of construction.

Three 250-feet high tower cranes were imported from France to raise the mighty concrete burdens into position for bonding into the whole. The cranes were supported on special cradles designed by Hornibrooks. Laid over the entire surface area of the shells are one million ceramic tiles — some sections glossy white and other sections matte buff colour — which reflect the silvering light from the sea and the varied brilliance of the sun. Manufactured in Sweden by Hoganas, the tiles measure 4¾'' by 4¾'' by ⅝'', and cover four acres of roofing. Of the 4,220 trays on which the tiles are set, the biggest weighs four tons and measures 33 feet by 7 feet 6 inches.

Sydney Harbour is filled with familiar sounds: the deep throated sirens of ocean liners, the hoots of tugs and ferries, the roar of power boat exhausts and the shrill cries of sea gulls. These sounds created noise problems

In the preparation of the
tile chevrons, the ceramic tiles
are laid face down and concrete
poured on to the backs to form a tray.
Prior to installation,
the tile face is sealed.
Then the completed trays are stored
awaiting placement.

With infinite care
the trays are positioned.
Like giant feathers laid
side by side,
they protect and add beauty
to the rising arches of
the shell roofs.

involving years of calculation and research before the architects and engineers were able to perfect the filling in of the gaping mouths of the roof shells and the sound-proofing of the halls and rooms.

The open end of each of the two largest vaults covering the Concert Hall and Opera House is closed with noise-resistant sheet and rib bronze with an inner lining of concrete. The many wall openings and the open mouths of other vaults are sealed with laminated amber-coloured glass panes imported from Boussois-Souchon-Neuvesel in France. The tinted glass was delivered in sheets and cut to size on the site on a machine specially designed in Australia. Installed, the panes vary from about 4 feet square to some 14 feet high by 8 feet 6 inches wide. Most are ¾" thick and consist of two layers, one plain, the other amber, bonded by a special interlayer for maximum sound exclusion.

There are 2,000 such panes in seven hundred different sizes, all computerised for accuracy of dimension by engineers from Ove Arup & Partners. They were cut and installed by VASCOB, a Sydney consortium of leading Sydney glass companies, Vetro, Astor, Sandys and O'Brien. Laid out side by side they would cover an area of one and a half acres.

The glass walls are supported on mullions of shaped steel members rising the whole height of the shell mouths. To these are attached bronze glazing bars into which the panes are set in a silicone putty to allow the glass to expand and contract.

Using tubular steel scaffolding built and erected by Cyclone (Aust.) Ltd. to support the special platforms required, the first pane was placed into position early in 1971, in the northernmost vault of the Concert Hall.

Reflecting the clouds above,
the tiling of the tallest shell
roof, A2, is completed
and the small shell roofs
are prepared for tiling.
Soon the commuters
on the harbour ferries
see the mighty structures
completed.

Looking at the Opera House
prior to the completion of the
podium steps and concourse.
From left to right
are Bennelong Restaurant,
the Concert Hall
and the Opera Theatre.
The finishing touches are put
to the pink granite aggregate paving
slabs covering the podium
steps and broadwalk.
The Ceremonial Steps
leading to the Opera Theatre
display the wide tread
and easy-rise access
to the Opera House
complex.

The Sydney Opera House
as it appeared from Farm Cove
in February 1973.

The Masterpiece

The Sydney Harbour
ferries and the hydrofoils
taking passengers
between the southern and northern
shores of Sydney Harbour witness
the final stages of completion
of the Opera House.

Patrons ascending the
broad Ceremonial Steps
pass the Bennelong Restaurant
before entering the
Concert Hall.

ON many occasions the Opera House will be taxed to its capacity when more than 7,000 people are attending performances, meetings, exhibitions, receptions and rehearsals all at the same time. Many will come to dine, others to stroll along the Broadwalk taking in the ever-changing harbour scene. Within the vast interior, staffs will be working to improve vision, sound and comfort which already reach a high degree of efficiency.

At the peak of construction, which was reached in mid-1972, more than 1,200 workers were engaged on the site, and at least as many more in factories producing materials and equipment. The entire project was a lesson in co-operation; everyone worked towards a common goal: the creation

Walls of glass
and walls of textured timber
meet in the sculptured
shell of concrete.

of a cultural complex more magnificent than the world had ever seen. Many of the workers were migrants to Australia. Each worker became an important cog in a vast cosmopolitan wheel of enterprise.

Materials and equipment were brought from many lands: exterior tiles from Sweden, interior tiles from Japan and Austria, curtains and stage lighting from Germany, carpets from New South Wales and Victoria, heat pumps from the U.S.A.; technical advisers were seconded from Philips of Holland and the General Electric Company of Britain.

A major triumph was achieved in the scientific perfection of sound in all the halls and theatres within the complex. With this objec-

tive, the design of the interiors and their furnishings was the subject of years of calculations, expert opinions and research, and in particular of tests by means of models — in which Dr. Wilhelm Jordan, a world authority, played an important part.

On December 17, 1972, as a test of acoustics, a concert was given by the Sydney Symphony Orchestra in the Concert Hall. The performance was conducted by Sir Bernard Heinze, to a capacity audience of workmen and others associated with the building. The result satisfied even the most exacting critics.

From the northern wall to the back wall of the stage, the curving grandeur of the vault-forming concrete ribs of the Concert Hall and the Opera Theatre is hidden from below by

Sealed from the
sounds of busy waterway,
of sea gulls and ships,
the shells of the Opera Theatre
look out on the harbour.

Opposite page:

The last rays of a setting sun
light the feathered tile 'chevrons'
covering the shell roof of
the Opera Theatre.

suspended fabricated "acoustic ceilings". The focal point of the Concert Hall ceiling is a crown piece of white birch plywood, 40 feet in diameter and 80 feet above the floor, containing many light sources. From this, panels of birch ply swirl out radially to form the bottom side of the hollow ceiling. Then they plunge vertically downwards to form the upper part of the walls of the hall. The lower part and the floor are finished in laminated brush box.

The 'mellow' acoustics so essential for symphony orchestral presentations in the Concert Hall, have been perfected to a two second reverberation time.

At the southern end of the Concert Hall the great organ, designed and being built by

Sydney's Ronald Sharp, will be installed. It will have more than 11,000 pipes and will be the largest mechanical action pipe organ in the world. Although it will not be completed until 1976, the huge instrument will be playable before that time.

Within the Opera Theatre, beneath the suspended ceiling faced with black-stained Australian carrabeen, almost every member of the audience has a clear view of the stage, whether seated in gallery, box or on the auditorium floor level.

The multi-tiered seating, in red leather upholstery, has been designed for comfort and in harmony with the magnificent tapestry curtain. The auditorium is attuned to the sound frequency of operatic singing, with a reverberation time of 1.4, and every note

Above the pink-clad
podium of the northern Broadwalk,
the sail roofs
of the Concert Hall reach
to the sky.

Opposite page:

The sweeping curve of the
Concert Hall roof.

reaches the audience in perfect quality of tone. On the stage, rapid changes of mood and scene are made possible by a revolving sector and travelling platforms.

On the stage at the southern end of the Opera Theatre, the warm yellows, reds, pinks and browns of the "Curtain of the Sun" cover the stage, an area of 1,404 square feet; 27 feet high by 52 feet wide. In it are woven the abstract designs of Queensland artist John Coburn. The delicate, intricate tapestry work was carried out in a small medieval French village near Aubusson, by the firm of Pinton Freres, using Australian wools and cotton.

In the Drama Theatre a subdued ceiling of black imperite-coated alumimium focusses all attention on the stage. Deep blues, greens and browns predominate in the "Curtain of the Moon", an equally striking sister to the "Curtain of the Sun". Measuring 64 feet wide and 17 feet high, it faces the vermilion wool-upholstered seats, the rich blue carpet and dark grey walls of the auditorium of the Drama Theatre.

The floor coverings for all the public areas were designed to complement the simple architecture of the interiors. They were made in Australia by F. & T. Carpets Pty.Ltd. which has since become Pacific Carpets International Pty.Ltd. Plain pure wool velvet pile carpets of Wilton construction were made in broadloom widths, mainly of 12 feet to minimise the number of seams. Six rich colours were chosen: for the Opera Theatre foyer, scarlet; for the Concert Hall foyer, deep purple; for the Drama Theatre, prussian blue. The Music Room and Exhibition Hall were carpeted in grey; the Reception Hall in emerald green; and the Restaurant in ochre. Altogether, covering an area of over two acres, about 10,000 square yards of carpet

John Olsen's mural —
a nocturnal study of Sydney Harbour —
measuring seventy feet long
by ten feet high,
dominates the Concert Hall
foyer.

The glassed ceiling and wall
look over Sydney's
northern shores.

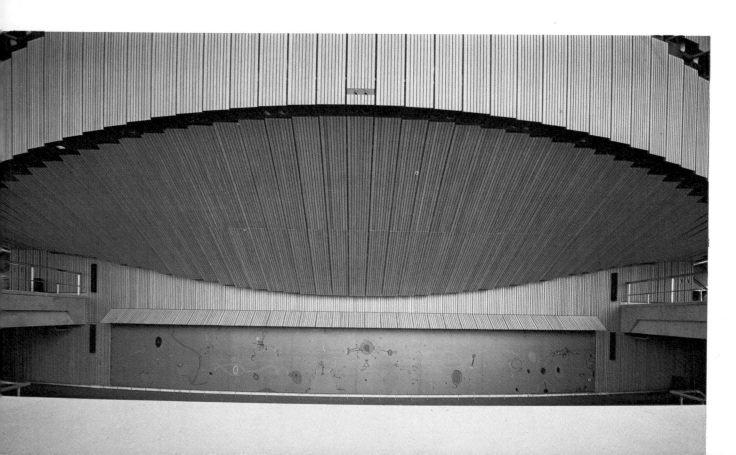

Adjustable acoustic 'clouds' above the Concert Hall platform.

were made. Dyestuffs with maximum fastness properties were chosen for the colour masters, against which the actual carpets were to be matched.

In order that the coverings might retain their rich, luxurious appearance under heavy wear, careful selection of the wool for the pile yarn was essential. Australian wools are normally too fine and soft for this purpose, and so a blend of British wools was chosen from crossbred and mountain types of sheep. This blend was similar to that used in the weaving of the magnificent carpet for the Coronation of Queen Elizabeth II in 1953.

The elaborate system of concealed lighting is a major feature of the Opera House, ranking in importance with the high fidelity sound amplifying equipment and its distribution network.

The Australian organisations of Philips of Holland and the General Electric Company of Britain joined in a consortium, known as G.E.C.-Philips Opera House Lighting Company Pty.Ltd., to design, manufacture, supply and instal both the interior and exterior lighting in all areas except the stages. It proved to be the largest and most complex lighting project ever undertaken in Australia.

Detailed studies were made of theatres throughout the world in order to benefit from international experience. No building,

however, had ever been faced with similar problems. Many Opera Houses are decorated with marble and gilt, large paintings and crystal chandeliers, all of which form part of the scene. The Sydney Opera House is completely opposed to any such flamboyancy. The building is massive, strong, dignified and quietly beautiful. The architecture provides many changing vistas, glimpses of the shells, curving beams, and foyers of constantly varying shapes, with granite floors and walls, concrete ceilings and timber panelling. The problem of "lighting" the vast interiors was not how to hang the fittings — but how to effectively illuminate overall the multitude of architectural features.

The ultimate plan was to light the approach areas in a very low key, build up the intensity in each area, high-lighting features of particular interest, and culminate with a visual climax in the auditoria. These objectives have been spectacularly achieved.

At night the shells are softly floodlit,allowing the interior to glow and give life to the building. Around the external broadwalks are large glass spheres on bronze columns, giving a warm yellow gleam reminiscent of the old gaslight days. The steps of the podium, the widest of their kind in the world, are lit by lamps concealed in the hand rails and by the soft floodlighting reflected from the shells.

Looking out
to the vast auditorium
from the organ loft
on the southern wall of
the Concert Hall.

The rising arches and vaulted
ceiling of the Opera Theatre.

Great care has been taken that the internal
lighting does not impare the superb views of
the Harbour through the windows.

Within the building closed circuit television is
programmed from the Opera Theatre, Concert Hall and Drama Theatre for the benefit of
late-comers who must wait in lounges or
foyers until the end of an act before they are
admitted to their seats.

Instant communication between floor levels,
rooms and halls is made possible by two
incoming-call exchanges and 350 extension

units. Numerous telephones are also
available to the public.

Electronic equipment, similar to that used in
the United Nations Building in New York,
makes almost instantaneous translations — five languages individually
relayed — in the Concert Hall and Opera
Theatre. In the Drama Theatre, Cinema and
Recital Room, three language translations
are possible.

The staging equipment, made partly in
Australia and partly in Vienna by Waagner
Biro A.G., was installed by Australians under

the direction of expert technicians from over-seas.

A huge air-conditioning plant, costing $3½ million, changes the air in the theatres eight times an hour, and clears the kitchens every two minutes.

In most countries of the world good food has become a part of modern life; an experience to be enjoyed. Thus in planning the Opera House complex, provision was made for high standard restaurants for the use of patrons wishing to dine before a performance, for supper afterwards and for the hundreds of sightseeing visitors wanting a quick snack.

On the Quay side of the podium, adjacent to the main entrance steps, is the main restaurant known as the Bennelong Restaurant. It is built on three levels: the upper and lower are for meals and the middle level is a bar.

On the Broadwalk, below the Opera Theatre, and overlooking the Harbour, is the self-service Harbour Restaurant to seat 150 people under cover and up to 300 in the open air. Like the Bennelong Restaurant it is fully licensed.

The "Curtain of the Sun" within the Opera Theatre.

Within the Drama Theatre
the "Curtain of the Moon" faces
out to vermilion seats and
dark blue carpeting.

The practice that brings
perfection.......

Opposite page:

Students of the N.S.W. State
Conservatorium of Music attend
the official ceremony of
the handing over of the
Recording Room.

In the foyers of the Concert Hall and the Opera Theatre are licensed buffets, serving food and beverages for their patrons. The Drama Theatre and the complex embodying the Music Room and the Exhibition Hall also have their own licensed buffets.

Many areas are available for receptions, business meetings, cocktail parties and buffet luncheons.

The catering service has been entrusted to Oliver Shaul, one of Australia's highly acclaimed restaurateurs, whose Summit Restaurant at the top of Australia Square is favoured by patrons from all parts of the world.

As well as the many halls, theatres and rooms which facilitate the performance of its primary functions, the complex holds many administrative offices, large and small rehearsal rooms, and fifty dressing rooms with individual ablution amenities. Here also is the Headquarters of the Sydney Opera House Trust. In all, there are more than 900 rooms in the complex.

There is no problem to which there is not a solution. And so it was with the Sydney Opera House — from its conception to the completion of the masterpiece. The solving of each new problem of design and construction brought a new proficiency, of benefit to architects, manufacturers, builders and technical scientists the world over.

The people of Australia are the richer for owning and sharing this mighty centre of culture which will be a source of creative inspiration to the performing arts for generation upon generation to come.

Financed by Lottery

The Board Room
of the Sydney Opera House
Trust.

DESIGNED for the people and built by private enterprises, the Sydney Opera House and the land on which it stands is owned by the State Government elected by the people of New South Wales. From its beginning, the project was guided by successive State Ministers of Public Works until its completion. Now a permanent managing body, the Sydney Opera House Trust, is responsible to the Minister for Cultural Activities for its administration and maintenance and for the presentation of performing arts of the highest standard.

The gigantic project has been financed by an Opera House Lottery, which together with funds raised through public appeals, will ultimately meet the entire $100 million now estimated to be needed to cover the costs of construction. The first lottery — tickets costing £3 ($6.00) each, with a major prize of £100,000 ($200,000) — was drawn on January 10, 1958, and at frequent intervals new lotteries of 100,000 tickets continue to be drawn.

The Sydney Opera House Trust

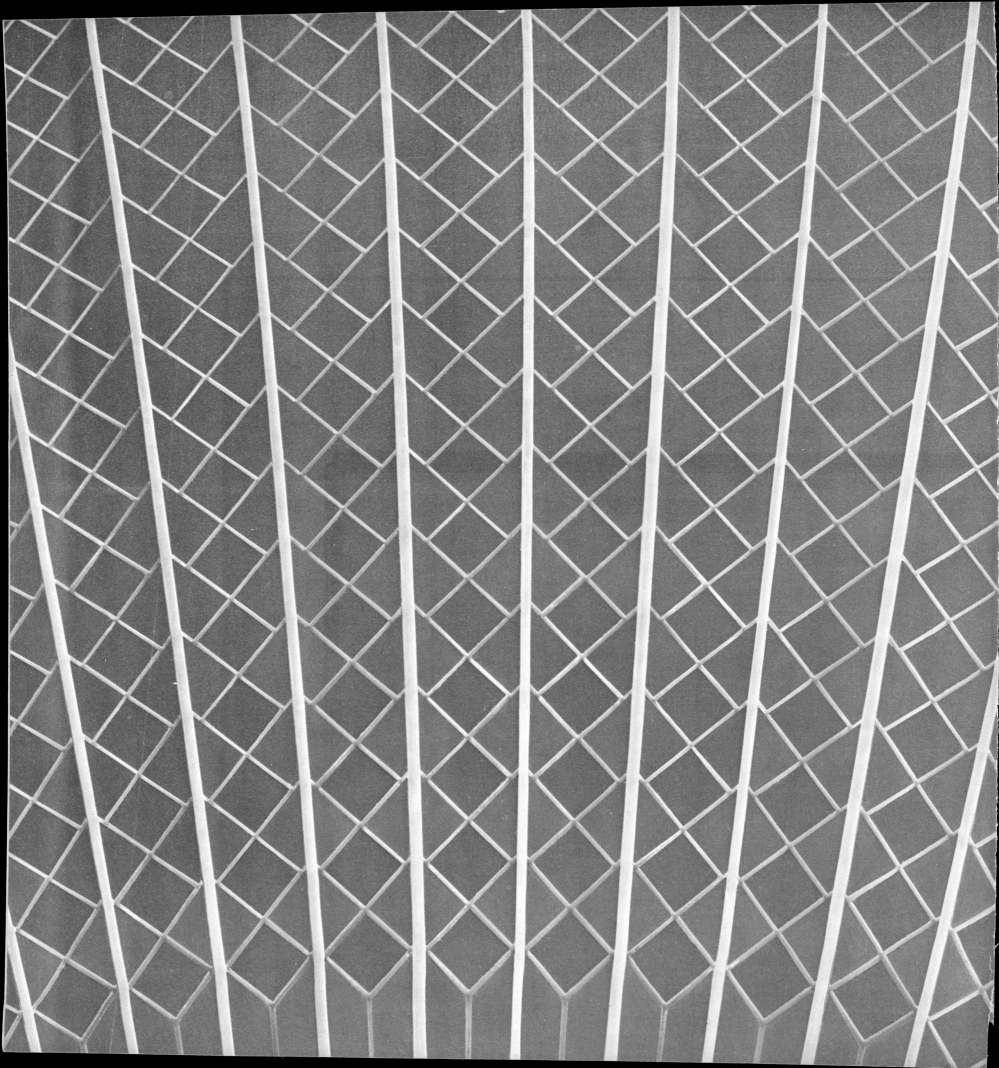